FLIBBERT
and
SKRIDDICKS

GW00359776

(Bits and Pieces)

Stories and Poems
in the
Devonshire dialect
by
Clement Marten

'Nathan Hogg' (Henry Baird)

'Jan Stewer' (A. J. Coles)

W. Gregory Harris

Jack Connabeer

William Weeks

May Crook

Including a glossary of nearly 200 dialect words

Peninsula
Press

First published 1983 by Clement Marten Publications

Republished as a revised and enlarged edition in 2002 by Peninsula Press,
an imprint of Forest Publishing
Woodstock
Liverton
Newton Abbot
Devon TQ12 6JJ

British Library Cataloguing in Publication Data

A catalogue record for this book is available from the British Library.

ISBN 1–872640–50–8

Editorial, design and layout by:
Mike Lang

Typeset by:
Carnaby Typesetting, Torquay, Devon TQ1 1EG

Printed and bound in Great Britain by:
Kingfisher Print & Design Ltd, Totnes, Devon TQ9 5XN

Contents

A Devonshire Prayer

Matthew, Mark, Luke and John,
God bless tha beyd that I lies on.
Vower cornders tu me beyd,
Vower angels lie aspreyed.
Tu tu vute an tu tu heyd.
An vower tu car me wen I'm deyd.
An wen I'm deyd an een me grave,
An all me boans be ratten,
Tha gready wurms me vlaish
wull ayte,
An I chell be vergotten.
Amen.

Matthew, Mark, Luke and John,
God bless the bed that I lie on.
Four corners to my bed,
Four angels lie aspread.
Two to foot and two to head,
And four to carry me when I'm dead.
And when I'm dead and in my grave,
And all my bones be rotten,
The greedy worms my flesh will eat,
And I shall be forgotten.
Amen.

Voreword

A vew volk kep' gwain awn t' me 'bout they ab'm got nort wot they c'n raid tu maitins. Yu naw, wen they 'as a do tu th' Institoot they likes ver zumbody, wot c'n spaik Dem' dialect, t' git up 'an raid 'em zummat een th' old spaich, like wot they dood yers agon wen they 'ad pinny raidins.

Well yers a vew items wot me an' a vew other volks 'av wrote. They wot t'others 'av wrote I put ther names tu'm. They items wot ab'm got no name pun tap yu c'n blame me ver'm – 'cuz I wrote they an broadcast 'm awn t'ole wireless backalong. I've put me 'nitials tu the bottom, zo'z yu naws they'm by me.

Een case any o' they vurriners wot can't spaik Dem' dialect – th' higgerant toads – gits 'olt o' wan o' thaise yer liddle bukes an' dawn naw wot zum o' th' words mains, I've put wot they calls a glossy tu th' back aend.

I aups as yu injoys thaise yer flibberts an' skriddicks.

Clem Marten

Voreword to the Second Edition

I t gives me great pleasure to know that my late father's book, *Flibberts and Skriddicks* (Bits and Pieces), has been given a further opportunity of being brought to the attention of those interested in the Devonshire dialect, especially as it has been carefully updated and enlarged with two or three additional stories.

Although my father managed to instil in me his love of archaeology and things historical, I have readily to admit that he didn't succeed with his interest and love of the Devonshire dialect. I do not, therefore, feel qualified enough to comment on the subject, but I should like to share with you some early recollections of my father.

As a small child I can remember him telling me stories of his younger days. One was of a school he went to in Plymouth, where only one child from a family could attend on any one day – for they had only one pair of shoes! Another was of the times when he used to go to St John's Hospital School (the Blue Boy school) in Exeter: every time I walk through Princesshay and see the Blue Boy, marking the entrance to the school, I always think of my father. He also used to tell me that in the summer months, when in his teens, he would cycle with a friend from Plymouth to Exeter, stay with his aunt for a few days, and then cycle back home to Plymouth. And yet another was of the time when he helped excavate a Roman floor mosaic, now housed in Exeter's Royal Albert Museum, with his friend, Arthur Everett.

In reading these little snippets of mine, I hope that you will find them of some interest, of a lifetime ago when things were very different. Some people might say the 'good old days'; I'm not so sure.

Sue Quick

May 2002

Introduction

During the last two hundred and fifty years, there have been many authors and poets who have written in the Devon dialect, all of whom have adopted their own form of orthography. Because of this, there is no accepted way of spelling dialect words other than to convey, in writing, the sound of the word in a way the writer learned it in childhood.

Some "dialect" writers were not true dialect speakers, but were people who developed an interest in the subject and wrote down what they thought they had heard, after listening to their gardeners or maidservants without really understanding the meaning or thinking that lay behind the words and phrases.

However, the stories and poems in the following pages have been selected because they were all written by dialect speakers. I have retained their individual forms of phonetic spelling, in order to demonstrate the variety and because I would not presume to alter what others have written.

I am sure that most Devon dialect speakers will have little difficulty in applying their own pronunciations when they read aloud the stories and poems. I urge them not to endeavour slavishly to interpret what they read, but instead to adopt those pronunciations and intonations which come naturally to them. Those readers who are not Devonians must do the best they can.

The locality from which the reader comes will determine the pronunciations or, in some cases, the meaning of words and phrases. For instance, in the poem, "A Bit o' Binder String" written by May Crook in East Devon, the use of the word "string" is not common throughout the county. The word "cord" is much more likely to be used.

An example of how the reader may exercise his or her individuality is in the poem, "The Better Plan" by William Weeks, in the third line of the fifth verse, "To thraw some light 'pon anything." The reader may choose to recite as I do, "T' draw zum light 'pon ort."

Clem Marten

1983

Our Dem'shur Spaich

W. GREGORY HARRIS

Our Dem'shur spaich du maake volks laugh, when they du visit we,
But us dawn't keer what *they* du think, – 'tez ignorance yu zee;
An' us b'ant gwain to maake a shaw o' cuttin' up our words
Tu plaize the numskulls what wud scat gude Saxon into sherds.

✻ ✻

'Twas back-along, in Alfred's time, a thousand years agone
The Dem'shur spaich wuz fust a-spawk, – zo I've yurd tell upon;
An' by his words, zo zoft an' sweet, zo draalin', an' zo zlaw,
No matter where yu vind un tu, a Dem'shur chap yu'll knaw.

✻ ✻

Our S's be all zads yu zee, an' all our F's be V's,
Us calls a "wops" a "appledrane" (tu mark un off vrom bees),
A bat us calls a "flittermouse", a cock, her be a "stag",
A tomtit ez a "heckamal". – a cormorant's a "shag".

✻ ✻

Us wipes our nawse wi' " 'andkerchers", us "apses" up the gaate,
Us blaws the vire wi' "bellises", an' "quots" down 'pon the zait;
When things be turned all "backsivore", us zays that us be "dalled",
An' us be always "vitty" when tu "vittles" us be called.

✻ ✻

Us "axes" when us wants a thing, we'm "wisht" when we be bad;
Our cats du "sclum", – and us du call a shower o'rain a "scad",
Us du belong, when "chucked wi' thu'st", gude zider vor tu drink,
Tho' ef us "clunks" too much yu knaw, they claps us in the "clink".

✻ ✻

Us comes "whoam" in the "dimpsey", when the "kittle's" 'pon the "bile",
An' if us mucks the "drexil" Missus "blares" in prapper style –
Vor her's a reggler "clapper-claw", an' always 'pon the "towse",
An' can't abide when volks traapse een tu "bissle" up th'ouse.

✻ ✻

Our wimmen-volk maakes "licky-brath", – et du go down zo suent,
An' all our "Passons" pray an' praich like "anyels", – they'm zo fluent;
Our "childern" what du go tu schule, be ter'ble fond o' "mitchin",
While "Vather's" at his "lousterin' "work, – a "datchin" an' a-ditchin'.

✻ ✻

Our "orchits" they be vull o' fruit, our vields they'm vull o' "whate",
An' gurt big mangel-wurzels, vor the "bullicks" vor tu ait;
Our gardens graw all kinds o' "traade", – an' 'tez a sight tu zee
Our clumps o' "bliddy-waryers" zo galliant as can be.

✻ ✻

The "boy's-love" sweet, us all du love, – the rawses all in "blooth",
The fragrant "harbs", an' violets a-shelterin' in the "lewth";
The "tetties", an' the "crilly greens", the "pays" an' "kidney-bains",
Bezides the "primrosen" an' sich a-grawin' in the laanes.

✻ ✻

Aw iss, 'tez "braave" down yer I zim, – our "mouth-spaich" may be quaint,
But it du zuit us all tu zay "I be", or else "I baint",
An' what's the odds 'bout grammar ef yu maake yer mainin' plain?
Us all du onderstand the chap who sez "I must be gwain".

✳ ✳

Zo "up-along", an' "down along", an' "whoam along" we'll go,
An' "een along", an' "out along", "a-traipsin' " tu an' fro;
An' as vor they there "dapper" chaps, zo mincin' in their spaich,
They a'nt got nort as I can zee us Dem'shur Volk tu taich.
An' yu may bet old Debbn's gwain tu hold her plaace of fame
Vor sturdy men, an' purty maids, – vor budder, an' vor craim,
Zo us will kaip our mouth-spaich pure, in spite o' what volks zay,
An' you shall yer it braave an' broad, when yu'm down Debbn way.

✳ ✳ ✳

Th' Zindy Scule Trait

Yer, did I tull 'ee bout thaise yer boys wat went awn a Zindy Scule Trait? Wull, they gits down awn th' zayzhore tu Exmuff* an they zides t'av a paddle. Zo they taaks auf ther boots an zocks an wun boy lukes t' t'other an ee says,

"Aw git awm Garge, ow bissley yer vit be."

An Garge says, "Oh ace, course they be, cuz I didn cum awn Zindy Scule Trait las' yer, zo I av'n ad no paddle een th' zay zince th' yer avore las'! That's why me vit be bissley this yer."

*or nearest seaside.

When Jan Played Football

AO COLES (JAN STEWER)

A. J. COLES ('JAN STEWER')

Don't talk to me about yer ole vootball. I've had all the vootball I wants, thank you. I took part in it once, and I bet a guinea I'll never do such thing again. How I come to be such a fule as to have aught to do with it, I can't think. However, it larned me a lesson, to laive alone things you don't understand; so I s'pose it done zome gude in a sort of a way. But 'twas a sort of a way I shude'n like very auf'n.

I'd no business bein' there, 't all. If I'd bide home about me work 'twude never have happened. But they made such a fuss about Muddlecombe parish havin' a vootball match, which such a thing had never happened bevore, that I must go and view it like the rest o' the gawks. Why they shude drop 'pon me like they did I can't tell 'ee, 'cus I never done none aw'm no harm that I knows by.

'Twas our chaps agin the Barleycombe chaps, and 'twas only natteral that us shude wish to zee the Muddlecombe lot ween, though what they had to do to bate the other lot I did'n know no more 'n Adam. I did'n know no more about vootball than a cat knows about his awn gran'mother. But I knows now, begad. At laiste, I knows all I wants to know, and in future I'll be satisfied to go down to the Black Oss and play rings. That's more in my line, and not so likely to spoil my buty.

'Twas a vine day fer't, so I pokied away down to Varmer Grant's ten-acre vield to zee this-yer vootball match they was tellin' so much about, never mis-trustin' nothin'. Soon's I got there, the feller they calls the cap'm come rishin' up to me in a joost of a swat.

"Jan," he says, "one of our chaps have bin took bad with a pain in his stommick and he can't play. You mus' come and take the place of 'en."

Of coorse, if I'd had any sainse I wude 'a-bin took bad with a pain in the stommick likewise, but I did'n think aw't in time.

I made all the excuse I cude think of, but they gurt mump'aids wude'n harken to me. They tooked me into Varmer's kitchen and trigged me out in a stoobid ole shurt, like Josep's coat o' many colours, and a li'l ole pair o' short burches which did'n raiche down to me knees. Wad'n hardly dacent, I don't reckon they was, not fer a man my age. I looked like one o' they zebra things, stood up on his hine legs.

"Whatever's the gude?" I says. "You'm only makin' fules o' yerzel's and me too. I dunnaw nothin' about yer ole vootball, and I don't want to vind out, nuther."

But I might as well knack me haid up agin the wall as spaik to they fellers.

" 'Tis fer the honour o' the parish, Jan," they said. "Us muzzen let they Barleycombe chaps crow over we. And there won't be very much fer you to do. Us don't want you to do no rinnin' about. Us wants you to be gold-keeper."

"That'll suit me zac'ly," I says. "You bring along the gold, I'll keep it."

Wull, so then the cap'm feller took me over-cross to where they gold paustis was to. They wad'n gold 't all. Only ole timbern paustis, that's all they was; two sticked up about a lan'yard apart, and one across the tap. He was up – aw, what wude he be? Wull, jist up where I cude'n raiche 'n, he was.

"Now, Jan," they said to me, "all you got to do is to bide yer and not let the ball go past 'ee."

"Sounds all right," I said. And nothin' more wad'n said about it.

Then the vootballin' chaps scattered theirzels about all over the plaace. Our lot was decorated up with blue and yaller strips across their chestis, and tother fellers had got rid and black. That's so they cude distinct one from tother. Then there was one li'l feller about half-ways up, he had'n got nothin' seps a wissle. What I mean to say, he had'n got none o' they purty colours. He only weared the zame togs what he had on every day. Only he had this-yer wissle and he keep bowin' chunes on 'en. What he was there 't all vor I dunnaw, cus he wad'n a particle o' gude, and only got in tother volks's way.

When they was all in raddiness, this-yer li'l feller blowed up a bit of a chune, and in one minute they was all rishin' about like a parcel o' rabbuts. I was glad as a burd they putt me in gold-keeper, cus I had'n got nothin' to do seps to watch the tother fellers rinnin' about.

Presen'ly I zee'd one li'l chap rinnin' along by hiszelf. Caw! I never zee'd anybody rin like it in my life. Gwain like one train, he was. One o' they rid and black fellers he was. Stranger to me. I never zee'd the feller bevore in me life that I knows by. But my days, he cude rin. And he'd got the ball along with 'n, too. Aw, 'ees. Ball and all.

Wull, then, sevver'l of our chaps went arter this-yer li'l feller to try and take the ball away from 'en. 'Twas our ball, mind. He had'n got no more right to 'en than what you have, not a bit more. But they cude'n ketch 'en. He was too vast fer they. Comin' right towards me he was, too, so I had a splendid view of 'en.

Wull, and I was takin' interest in this-yer li'l chap. I was lookin' to zee how fur he cude rin like it. However, when he thought he'd rinned fur nuff he stapped, and up with his voot, and he gived a kick to thikky ball – My dear zaul! If he did'n zend 'en jis' like a shot out from a gun. Wull, went right past where I was to. So that'll show 'ee.

Mind you, I thought the feller might jist as well look and zee where he was kickin' of 'n to. 'Twas very careless of 'en, kickin' of 'n so close to me. 'Cus 'twad'n as if he did'n know I was there. 'Twas the luckiest thing in the world I wad'n stood a bit further over. If I had 'a-bin I shude never have escaped 'n.

Wull, then all they rid and black fellers started jumpin' up and down and holleyin' out, "Gold, gold." Proper delighted with theirzels they was. What vor I dunnaw. But our chaps come around me and started spaiken' proper cross to me. Spesh'ly that-there cap'm feller. Properly rude I reckon he was.

"Why had'n 'ee stop 'n, Jan?" he says. "Why had'n he stop 'n?"

"Stop what?" I says.

"Why, the ball, yer silly fule. Why, fer gudeness' sake, had'n 'ee stop 'n?"

"If he wanted me to stop 'n," I says, "why did'n he kick 'n yer, where I cude raiche 'n, not all out there, zix voot away."

"Aw, you gurt gawk," he says. "He don't want 'ee to stop 'n, but us do. You must dap about a bit and not let the ball go past 'ee."

"Wull, why had'n 'ee told a feller zo? But 'tis no gude you vindin' fau't with me. You want to spaik to that li'l rid and black feller. He kick 'n, I did'n."

With the zame the feller in the middle blowed up another chune on his wissle, and away-to-go, worse 'n ever.

Bim-bye I zee'd the zame li'l chap comin' again. Ball and all.

"All right me li'l feller," I says. "Not this time."

So I went over where I considered the ball was comin' to – well, zame place he come bevore, then, and I got mezelf all in raddiness for 'n and spraid out me arms. But do you know, that li'l chait (that ever I shude say sitch thing), instead of he kickin' the ball to me as he shude 'a-done, he kick 'n zide ways. Wull, there was another rid and black feller stood over there. He wad'n nothin' to do wai't, he wad'n. 'Twas me and the li'l chap, zee.

Wull, and o' cou'se, the other feller he putt his voot to the ball and jis' touched 'n, and in he goes, right droo the gold. There wad'n nothin' to stop 'n.

Then all they rid and black fellers started dancin' up and down again, and holleyin' "Gold, gold."

"Yer," I says, "that wad'n fair," I says. "I wad'n lookin' that way."

"Aw," they said, "you mus' be lookin' every way."

"How many pair of eyes do a feller have on thees job, then?" I says. "What you wants yer is a spider."

Arter that there wad'n a minute's paice. They rid and black chaps was better vootballers than what our fellers was and they keeped on comin' down and tryin' to kick the ball droo my gold. Spesh'ly that li'l feller they called inzide-out. A proper nuisance he was, 'cus he wad'n satisfied when he'd done it once. He must keep on comin' and tryin' to do it again.

"Why don't that li'l feller sit down," I says, "and let zome other body have a go at it?"

"Aw," they says to me, "he played fer the Cristial Palace once."

"Aw, did 'er?" I says. "Well, if he rinned about like he have to-day he deserved to get it, too."

Wull, twad'n very long bevore I zee'd Mr. Inzide-out comin' again, and zame time I zee'd his partner comin' along with 'n.

"I'll be upzides with 'ee this time," I says. So what I done, I went over to one zide, jis' pretendin' like, till I zee'd the li'l feller was gwain to kick 'n across to his partner. The minute he putt his voot to the zide o' the ball I dapped across tother zide, just in time – wull, purty near.

But not quite.

You zee, where 'twas to, 'twas like this-yer. I wad'n hardly so dapper gettin' across as what I ordained fer to be, and that feller give the ball a kick like a mule.

I wad'n quick nuff to stop 'n with me hands.

I stop 'n with me faace.

BANG.

Aw, my dear zaul! I thought it never wude be a faace again. I did'n know what had happened. I cude'n zee; ner I cude'n yer; ner I cude'n spaik. I putt up me hand to the back o' me haid to zee if me nawse had come out behind.

And when I beginned to braithe again and got one eye open the cap'm feller come up to me and said:

"Bravo, Jan; bravo. You stopped that one butiful."

"Aw," I says. "What did I stop?"

"Why, you stopped the ball."

"Is that all? I thought I'd stopped a sharrybang."

"Look out, Jan. They'm comin' again."

"Aw, be um?" I says. "Wull, you come and putt your faace yer. I'm takin' mine home."

✳✳✳

'Bout me Ringworms

Yer, me luvvers, I be gwain t'tull ee bout me ringworms – chillern dawn zim t'git em like wat they did backalong wen I wuz a boy een t'1920's. I wuz livin een t'Exter then and I got ringworms awn me niddick – ver t'vurriners wat dawn spaik vitty Debm, me niddick be th' back o' me neck.

Now thaise yer ringworms wuddn gaw way naw matter wat th'ole doctor or th' Scule Clinic do'd tu'm. They put awn zum ole graizey cauch wat zmill'd like an ole daid cat an they dabbed awn a lot uv ole powders, but nort didn do no gude. Still I ad me ringworms awn me niddick waik arter waik.

Then cum th' time ver me olidays long wi me Granver and Granma, wat lived tu Whitestone wat's aun t'road vrum Bude tu Lansen. Wen I got ther, me Granma zaid,

"My dear Laurd, wativvers th' matter wi th' boy's niddick?"

"Ringworms," I zaid.

"Zo tiz," says she, "us'll av t'git Granver t'charm mun away ver ee."

Now this wuz zummat bout me Granver I didn naw nort bout. Zims ee ad "The Gift" – ee cud charm away ringworms an warts an volks cum vrum miles roun ver t'av em charm'd away be me Granver.

Ee didn only do this yer charmin on volks, but on calves az well. Zims calves iz prone tu ringworms an varmers vrum all roun used tu draive ther calves tu me Granver's gaate een vront o' eez cottage, ver t'av th' ringworms charm'd away vrum auv ther backs.

Nobody didn think this yer charmin wuz whisht, they jist nawd me Granver ad th' Gift, cuz ee wuz th' zeventh zon uv a zeventh zon. Ee wuz call'd Daniel 'Am an ee wuz born'd tu Kilkhampton.

Now wen me Granver zeed me ringworms on me niddick, ee zaid I wuz tu git zum ood ash, wat volks d' call "wood ash", ef they'm tryin t'spaik vitty. Anyways, I ad tu gaw an git this yer ood ash een me 'and an giv't tu me Granver een eez 'and, then ee stude be'ind me an ee zpat awn th'ood ash an mix'd uv't een tu a paste – at th' zame time, ee wuz mumblin an maunderin tu eezel a zort uv liddle prayer – then ee dabb'd this yer paste awn tu me niddick – yu naw, me neck – then ee says,

"Now yu bide still a liddle wiles an daun ee gaw titchin uv't wi yer vingers."

Now yu may vind this yer ard t'belaive, but dree days later ther waddn naw zign uv no ringworms awn me niddick – jist like they addn nivver bin ther an vrum that day awn, I didn nivver git no more.

Well ther me luvvers – that's all bout me ringworms.

C.M.

The Better Plan

WILLIAM WEEKS

Young Tom, the farmer's man, one night
Was going down the lane,
Candle and lantern in his hand,
To meet his Mary Jane.

✳ ✳

Now, as it happen'd, farmer Giles
Was coming up the lane,
And meeting Tom with lantern asked:
"Why, Tom, where be 'ee gwain?"

✳ ✳

Tom, looking sheepish, answered, "Zur,
Sure you knaw where I'm gwain –
" 'Tis courtin' night an' I'm jist off
To meet my Mary Jane."

✳ ✳

"But take a lantern courtin', Tom!
You be a quare young spark!
I always thort that soort o' thing
Was better in the dark."

✳ ✳

"Wull, maister, I 'ave always yerd
'Tis var the safest plan
To thraw some light 'pon anything
That you may take in 'an'."

✳ ✳

"Fudge! I'd no light to court my wive
When 'er was Nancy Ridd."
Sez Tom: "To jidge by the looks o' 'er, zur,
I shouldn' think you did!"

✳ ✳ ✳

Tom's Balanced Ration

MAY CROOK

A venin all. Ow be gwain awn then? I be awn me own tonight – Missus ave gone off tu thais yer ole Wimmins Institoot.

"Wimmins Institoot," I says tu she, "Prapper gabbin party, I reckon tis jis excuse ver all yu wimmin t'zup tay an gossip." Cor! Her spurred up like a broody aen.

"Tiddn naw sich theng," her zaid, "Us don't gossip a quarter 'alf so much as yu maen down tu Tuckers' Arms,* an look at all th' usevul thengs wat us do larn, too!"

"Oh ace" I says, "Yu mid do zummat useful now an then, I grant ee. But if wimmin do's one thing sensible, they do's dree things mazed – tis their nature, I reckon. Like they food values yu did larn bout – do ee mind?" Ha, ha, ha.

That made she prapper spiteful, an her went out an slammed th' door. Er can't abide tu be reminded o' that 'sno! I'll tull ee ow twer. They ad a talk one time down tu thic Institoot bout salads an food values an sich like. Missus wer vule o't nex mornin – ow bread an tiddies wuz vule o' starch an Carby 'Idrates or zummat, an mate an chaise wer vule o' Protaynes, an greenstuff wer vule o' they Vytamines, an ow yu did orter av zum of each of em een yer grub.

"Tom" her says, "I baint bin feedin ov ee right. Vrom now awn I be gwain t'give ee prapper balanced rations."

"Balanced rations?" I says, "What ee think I be? A battery aen or a bacon pig? Yu go on veedin I zames usural an nivver mind all thic ole nonsense."

Wull, when I come een t' me dinner, twer a steak an kidney pudden, wi mashed tiddies an cabbage. Alright it we too, till I starts on me cabbage.

"Yer" I says, "Missus, wa'vee done t' thais yer cabbage? Tis purt near raw!"

"Naw taint" er says, "Tis wat they calls consarvitivly cuked, wi all th' Vytamines een, stead o' stooed tu a mash an all th' goodness poured een pig tub, like I'v bin doin of. Yu ate it, tis a sight better ver ee that ways".

"Now look ee yer" I says, "I ates me food ver t'injoy it, not to be do'd good tu. I likes me cabbage stooed to a mash, as I don't care if this yers

* or nearest inn.

cuked Consarvative, Labour or Libral, tis orrible an I shan't ate it. Yu c'n chuck it all een pig tub.

"Aw, yu contrary ole toad" er says. "Now thic mayl baint balanced vitty, an I shall av t' make it right wi yer supper."

Wull, I wer over tu a sale at Dunkes'well thic arternoon, an yu naws ow wind do blaw up ther, takes two t' shet a gate up ther it do. I wer late wi me milkin an be th' time I got een 'ouse I wer fair starvin.

"Wa'vee got ver supper, me dear?" I say. "I ope tis zummat good, ver I be that 'ungry I c'd ate a bullick."

"Ther yu be" er says, an daps down a dish. "Bootivul that is – all vule o' Vytamines t' balance all thic starch yu ate tu yer dinner."

I looks tu it an twer nort but a mess o' greenstuff, wi a bit o' baitroot, all covered wi zummat slimy. An curled roun een th' middle wer a gashley lookin grey thing, ver all th' world like a gurt slug – oh Lor! Vair made I urge t' look tu it.

"Missus?" I says, "Be ee mazed? Whativer on hearth be this yer?"

"Tis a prapper balanced mail" er says, "Tis vule o' Vytamines, an ther be a pickled 'errin ver Protayne, an tis dressed wi hoil an vinigar. I nivver ad no salad hoil, zo I used a drap o' castor hoil out o' thic bottle yu ad ver t' drench th' calves – I spect twill do jist zo wull. An tis arranged careful wi light green lettuce an dark green nasturtium leaves, an egg, an baitroot ver a bit o' colour, cuz Miss Jones wat giv'd th' leckcher zed twer vurry himportant t' plaise th' heye as wull as yer stummik.

"*Miss* Jones is er?" I says. "Wull if that's wat er do call a good mail, I reckon zum poor veller av ad a lucky escape. Plaise me heye an me stummik! I tull ee the sight o' thic ther do maake me heye blink an me stomach aive up! Take it away ver mercy sake! Gie t' th'ole sow! I don't naw bout er heye, but I reckon er stomach be stronger'n mine. An gie us a crust off ov thic loaf an a bit o' chaise an onion – twill plaise me heye an me stomach a sight bettern' thic mess."

Missus snatches up dish lookin vit t'cry.

"Yu'm a nasty hungratevule gurt brute" er says. "Yer be I, doin me best t'vaid ee prapper an kape ee wull, an all yu do's is t'maake mock. Tiddn naw use t'try an do good tu ee," er says an er sniffs a bit.

"Now me dear" I says, "ver nigh awn vourty yer yu'v ved I on good grub, cuked prapper an daycent, an I an't nivver bin bad t'baid een me live, cept wen mare bolted an fling'd I off dungcart, an that wernt thy vault. Yu don't nade naw young maiden vrim one o' they colleges t'taich ee ow t'vaid thee usband, cuz yu do's it right wull as tis. Now zittee down an us'll av a dish o' tay."

Er cheer'd up a mite, then, an poured out th' tay. Presently I zeed er lookin at me plate, thoughtvule like.

"Tom" er says, "I'v bin a-thinkin. Yu'v agot braid, wat be Carby Hydrates, an chaise, wat be Protayne an thic raw onion be vule o' they Vytamines, baint it?"

"So yu do say" I says, wi me mouth vule, "I can't zee em. Wat bout it then?"

"Why" er says. "Doan ee zee? Yu'v got a "balanced ration" arter all!"

I tull ee – wimmin! They'll awiz av th' las word zomehow, won't em?

❋ ❋ ❋

Jan Tremlett in Town

A. J. COLES ('JAN STEWER')

Ole Jan Tremlett had been stopping into Exeter fer a week on a visit to his married darter. Nellie, her name was, and I knawed her from a child. Nice maid her was, too, and as smart as one yer and there. Married very well, her did, 'cus old Jan gived her the very best eddication, I will say that for 'en. Sent her away to boarding-skule, he did, fer a twulve-month, to be finished off.

I dunnaw exac'ly what her husband do's, fer his living, but he don't bissle his hands, anyway. Works with his head he do, and have worked all the hair off the top. Proper up-to-date volks they be, and Nellie have turned into a rale town's laady, by all accounts.

But ole Jan he's one o' the gude ole-vashin soort. Orwis was and orwis will be. Go'th out in the vields every day along o' the men, and stands in and do's a day's work with the best aw'm, although he've no call to do it, so fur as the money part's consarned. But 'tis his 'obby. And when he cometh home, aiv'mins, he likes to have a bit of a waish and brish up and sit down in chimley cornder and yarn with anybody that likes to come along. Rough and raddy he is and gude as gold.

But he can't a-bear a lot of ole sarrymony, and bowing and scraaping, and togging up and all that sort o' thing; 'cus he've never been 'customed to it.

"I tell 'ee, soce," he says, arter he got back from Exeter, "if twad'n my own flesh and blid I wude'n go neast the place. 'Tis nothing short of a trial fer a plain body like I be. I dersay 'tis all right fer they what likes that kind o' thing, and I be very glad to think that my Nell shude be happy and have everything her wants, and a butiful houze and purty things to full it up with. But I was orwis born and bred where there wad'n no rume to spare fer nothing that had'n got some use to it."

"But laur bless yer zaul, they town's volks litters up their rumes with a passel of ole nick-nacks and jim-cracks and tinkeraments, no gude to man or baste, till there id'n rume to turn about, hardly. And 'tid'n to say they'm han'some, neether. Her'd got about a dizzen li'l rid devils stood up on the mantelpiece in the sitting-rume, with their tongues poked out."

" 'Why, Nell,' I says, 'whatever makes 'ee have sitch things about, cheel? 'Tid'n dacent.' "

" 'Aw,' her says, 'they'm novel.' "

"What do that mean, maister?" says Tom Zalter.

"I can't tell 'ee, zac'ly, Tom, but from what I can make out 'novel' mus' mean 'hugly.' Her'd got a' 'orrid gurt cloamen toad with the mouth of 'en wide ope', and gurt staring eyes purt' near jumping out of his head; and her said thik was novel. And her had a glassen man with a face like the warming-pan and his nose like the hannle of 'en, grinning like a gawk, with a belly like a barreel and legs like a frog. And he was novel, too. So I reckon novel must mean hugly."

"I dersay you'm right, maister," says Tom, " 'cus I yard the passen say once that Mrs. Chamsey had got her head full o' novel idayas, and her's hugly 'nuff, gudeness knows."

"You daun't fancy you'd like to live along o' the town's volks altogether, then, maister?" says Jim Tozer.

"No, ti-no! I'd sooner live out in pigs'-looze. Too much o' they ole vorms and sarrymonies, altogether. Out yer in co'ntry a feller can do what he mind to: go out when he likes and come in when he plaize, and wear whatever togs he thinks fit. But in there, gude laur, you got to be all the time stidding what other volks will think about 'ee. They made me putt a hard ole coller round me neck fus' thing o' the morning, and keep 'en there all the blessed day. And not Zindys only, but every day o' the wik. Every time I wanted to turn my haid 'twas like cutting my years off."

"And then the stoobid way they goes about their meals. 'Pon me zaul, I never knowed fer certain what meal I was aiting."

"Did'n 'ee, sure?"

"I did'n, sure. To start with, they never thinks about getting up mornings till the day is half auver. Fust morning I was there I got out o' bed the proper time and dressed mezelf, and went down over stairs; and there I was poking about fer I dunnaw how long all by mezelf, with not a saul about. Arter a nower or two the sarvant maid come along, and I found mezelf getting in her way every wip and turn. 'Twas wretched, 'twas railly; so arter that I use to bide up to-bed till the rest of 'em was about."

"So when it shude a-bin brexis-time by gude rights, the sarvant maid wude carr' me up a dish o' tay and a bit o' braid-'n'-budder. And then when 'twas knocking-along towards fore-noons' time they'd have their brexis, so-called. 'Genst us had finished that 'twude be up-home to nine o'clock; best part o' the day gone and nort done."

"Well, then, along about of one o'clock I yeard the rattle of knives and vorks, and I thought to mezelf, 'Now us be gwain to have dinner.' "

"But laur bless yer zaul, zomebody kicked up a most hawful racket on a sort of a bell contraption which they terms a gong, and darned if Nell did'n holley to me, 'Come in to lunch, dad.' "

" 'Gude heab'ms above,' I thought to mezelf, 'be us only now come to lunch? Why, dinner waun't be till dree or vower o'clock.' "

"However, us had lunch; but Nellie's husband wad'n there, 'cus he starts away mornings and daun' get back home again bevore aiv'min. And mind you, I thought 'twas a lot of unnecessary fuss and bother, jis' fer lunch. None o' yer hunch o' braid and chaise in yer hand, and a mug o' zider; but half-a-dizzen knives and vorks a-piece, and plates and dishes nuff fer a ridgement o' sawjers."

"Wull, us got that over, and the time went on, and about vower to half-past I yerd the dishes rattling again, so I thought to mezelf, 'Now 'tis dinner; but my gudeness gracious, what a time of day to be having it.' And I'd jist made up me mind that I wude take Nellie to tackle fer letting things get behind so disgraceful, when her called to me out in the garden: 'Tay's ready, daddy!' "

"Chaited 'ee out o' yer dinner, than, maister?" says Tom.

"Zac'ly what I thought in me awn mind, Tom. 'Lunch and then tay,' I said to mezelf; 'I suppause thase town's volk daun' have no dinner, and that's how 'tis they'm so thin and thurdle-gutted.' "

"However, I went in and sot down. But 'twad'n worth-a-while, 'pon me zaul. 'Twas only making a fule of a man's stummick. Her give me a cup o' tay – well, I was 'feared to putt it to me mouth, 'fraid I shude swaller cup and all. And the teeny-weeny bits o' braid-'n'-budder was that theen, that if you putt 'em two-double and folded 'em in half you'd got all yer work cut out to make two bites of 'em. I did'n feel a scrap hungerd when I started, but time I'd vinished I cude have eat a man off his hoss. So the only thing now, was to look vorward to zupper."

"And did 'em give 'ee a gude zupper, Mr. Tremlett?" says Mrs. Endycott.

" 'Old 'ard, missis; all in gude time, as the feller said when he was being say-sick and zomebody ax'd him if the anchor was up yet. Bim-by, Frank come home, and I thought to mezelf, 'Now us'll zoon have a bit o' zupper, 'cus he sure to be hungerd.' "

"And sure nuff, I yeard the old dishes and plaates rattling again, and very zoon the sarvant maid kicked up another racket on the old bell-thing. Or, 'twad'n a bell, really spaiking. 'Twas a gurt brassen thing, like a warming-pan without a hannle, and the maid let into 'en with a stick with a gurt knob on one end, like Zammy Ozegude has to wack the big drum with. You cude year the blessed thing all down the strate; and there wad'n no occasion fer it, 'cus us was all there handy, only waiting fer the chance."

"Zo I suppause you had yer zupper thees time, maister?" says Tom.

"Well, you can suppause again then," says the ole feller. "I'd gone up-over stairs to waish and make mezelf look a bit vitty-like, 'cus I zee'd they two had togged theirzel's up smart. And darned if Nell did'n call up to me:

'Come along, dad; dinner's ready!' "

"My hyvers! You cude have knocked me down with a straw-mot. I thought they must have all gone mazed, every wan of 'em. In bed at brexis-time; brexis at lunch-time; lunch at dinner-time; tay at no time at all; and now, when a chap was thinking about having a bit o' zupper and gwain to bed – dinner!"

"I shude'n a-thought 'twas gude fer 'ee to ait a hearty meal that time o' night," says Mrs. Snell. "The docters says 'tis very hurtful to have a heavy meal jist as you'm gwain to bed."

"Daun't talk about gwain to bed!" says Jan. "I cude zee now why they cude lie a-bed mornings and let the zin scorch their eyes out. Why, laur bless me, when us had vinished dinner Frank says: 'Well, what wude you like to do this aiv'min?' "

" 'This aiv'min' mind 'ee; and 'twas then gone eight o'clock."

"So then us went into the drawing-rume as they calls it (why for, I daun't knaw) and Nell her played the peanner a bit, and zinged a bit, and Frank he zinged, and zometimes they zinged both together. And there us zot, musicking and zinging and telling, till past leb'm o'clock. And at last I said: 'Whatever time do 'ee go to bed, cheel?' "

" 'Aw,' her says, 'us most-times goes off about half-arter-leb'm unless 'tis anything speshul.' "

" 'Bless my zaul', I says; 'I shude want dree howers' sleep by that time, purt' near.' "

"And did 'um have their meals like that every day, Mr. Tremlett?" says Mrs. Snell.

"Every day same."

"I suppause you got use to it, come-to-last?"

"No, ti-no. A man don't lost the habits of zixty years in a vortnight. Many's the morning when Nell did'n knaw I was outzide the houze I've flipped around to the li'l public-houze in the nex' strate and called fer a glass o' beer and a hunch o' braid and chaise. If it had'n been fer that, I do believe I shude have fergot me awn name and derections."

Cap'n Tope an' me Uncle

Yers agon, wen zailin ships wuz still tradin, I ad a uncle wat wuz cap'n uv eez awn schooner an e zail'd out uv Plymouth.

Uz awiz call'd'n "The Skipper". E wuz wat they used t'call a "vine vigger uv a man". E used t'wear one o' they caps wi a shiney black peak tu't, and e ad a big mustash an eez vace ad all the zigns o' vourty yers uv zayvairin on't.

E awiz wear'd a blue zarge zuit an a blue gurnsey – they nivver call'd em jerseys een Plymouth een they days – twaz awiz a gurnsey. Pun tap o' that e wear'd wat e call eez weskit an vrum one pocket uv eez weskit t' t'other pocket, wuz anged eez watch chain crost eez belly.

I c'n mind that th' Skipper ad eez ship's store near Phoenix Wharf down be th' Barbican, near wer they Pilgrim Vathers zail'd vrum. Ooz vathers they wuz I abb'm nivver yerd, but tiz zaid az ow they went on a bit uv a ways-goose t'Americky.

Now ther wuz a vew other skippers wat used t'mait up wi me uncle an they used t'av a vew draps o' this an that wen they wuz een Plymouth. One o' these yer skippers wuz call'd Cap'n Tope an like me uncle, ee lived over t'Oreston crass th' Cattewater. Een they days, uz call'd it Osen, but ef yu wants ver t'spaik vitty, yu calls it Oreston, but not Orreston, az I yerd zum vurriners zayin.

Anyway I'm gittin way vrum me story bout Cap'n Tope an me uncle. Now Cap'n Tope's missus wuz wat yu'd call a bit uv a 'clapper claw'. Er didn av naw truck wi drinkin an zich carrin awn, an if Cap'n Tope wuz t'cum awm a bit th' wuss ver wear, Mrs. Tope'd giv'n wat ver an tull eez vortune ver'n. Now one time me uncle, wat wuz call'd Cap'n Maynard, an Cap'n Tope ad ad a bit uv a skinvule een tu Plymouth an me uncle ad a job gittin Cap'n Tope on th' little steam verry, wat rin'd vrum Phoenix Wharf t'Turnchapel an then awn t'Oreston.

Anyways, een th'aend they landed on th' pier at Oreston an me uncle tell'd Cap'n Tope that eed betterway cum awm long uv ee an not let Mrs. Tope zee'n wen ee waddn zackly. Cap'n Tope zaid, "Th' missus'll be worritin wer I'm tu eef I baint awm dreckly." Me uncle zaid, "Wull uz'll gaw up your 'ouse an yu c'n ide roun th' cornder wile I tulls yer missus that yu'v ad tu gaw an zee yer shippin agent an yu'll be awm be th' nex verry."

Zo up they gaws an Cap'n Tope ides roun th' cornder an me uncle bangs on th' door an out cum Mrs. Tope. Me uncle tulls eez tale, ow Cap'n Tope is still een tu Plymouth wen vrum roun th' cornder cums a voice z'louds a vog orn – "Ha ha ha, yu gurt maized aid, yer I be roun th' cornder – I baint een tu Plymouth."

Wi' that, Mrs. Tope gi' me uncle a luke that ud av split Laira Bridge een two an out er gaws, kitches holt Cap'n Tope be eez yer an marches ee een doors.

Me uncle kep out uv Mrs. Topes way ver a week er two arter that an ee didn zee much o' Cap'n Tope neither.

Wull I got t' be gwain awn now, I can't stop tullin tu ee no longer, zo wish ee well me luvvers.

C.M.

'Arry's visit to a County Cricket Match

JACK CONNABEER

Us'd vinished up th'arvest purty early this yer, an when I rinned up 'gainst ole 'Arry Vinnicombe t'other day, I zez too'n "Yer 'Arry", I zez, "wot 'bout gwain up too Tawnton to zee a proper cricket maich. Zumerzet be playin' Middlezex, to zee witch au'm gwain too be champshun."

Ole 'Arry ee tooked auf ees 'at, 'n scretched ees aid. "Aw, I dunno", ee zez, "I an't niver bin too a proper cricket maich avore, zides I daun naw nort 'bout it."

"Aw, dawnee worry 'bout that", I zez, "I'll tell ee wot theym a'doo'n uv as theym gwain vore. Us'll laive 'ome atter breakfuss, an us aught too be 'ome 'bout ap pass sebm."

"Yer, wait a minute", ee zez, the contr'y ole toad, "wot 'bout milkin' me cows een th'arnoon, 'zides yoo naus wot a titchy ole toad Daisy is, er woan let nobody else titch er 's'naw." Ee wuz meanin' wan uv ees cows, 's'naw, ony ees missis is called Daisy, too.

"Aw dawnee be zo awkerd", I zez, "Missis ken milk'um, tell er give ole Daisy two, dree uv they there cabbige wot the mascals ev bin aitin, when er goes to milk'n."

Ee took auf ees 'at sivrel times more'n scretched ees aid, youd'a thought ee ad more vlays een ees aid then thur be on a vuzz-peeg. Still 'ventually ee zed ee'd go.

Cum Zaturday vornoon I drauve auver to ees varm to pick'n up. Cawm yoo'd a thought ee was gwain 'way fer a vortnight to yer Daisy tellin' too'n.

"Now Dad", er zez, 'er allus calls'n Dad 's'naw. "I've a packed ee up zum mayte een yer nawse-baig, cost I naws ow ungry yoo gets. Thers zum braid'n' chayse an two-dree payces uv daugh caake fer crib-time. Now fer dinner I've put ee een a rabbit pasty an a payce uv yesday's zuet puddn. An ver aafters I've gived ee two gurt apple dumplins. Aw, ees, I put ee een a jam-jar vull uv craym too ayte widdum. Eef yoo veels ungry cum middle uv th'arnoon I've gived ee dree-vower 'ome maade buns an a gert payce uv flap-jack, an aaf a loave of brayde an a jar uv 'uney. I 'ain't gived ee nort too drink 'cus I zeed ee een cellar drawin a jar uv zider."

"Now Dad", er zez, "Do ee think you'll be awright, ev I gived ee 'nough too ayte." "Ees", ee zez. Then er turned too me. "Yer Jan", er zez, "doan'ee let'n go en a pub an go drinkin beer en spirits, cos ees nort but a biddle-aided ole vule eef ee goes drinkin ort else arter ees zider."

Anyhow us got too the cricket ground betimes. Caw there wus underds of volks gwain een too. Us found a gude plaace'n sot down jist as the umpires paaked out too middle uv the vield.

"Wot be they docters doin yer", zez 'Arry. "They ban't docters", I zez, "Theym yer to zee vair play."

'Peers Middlezex won the toss, an made Zumerzet bat fust. When the two opening batsmen got too the wicket, 'Arry zez "Wot ev they got all that trade tied on their legs ver." "Aw thats case they gets knacked bee the baal." "Why? is'n that ard", ee zez. "Aw ees", I told'n, "ees ard's a dowgs aid."

Anyway bee this time 'Arry started too muzzle een ees nawse-beg. "Must be crib-time in-it", ee zez. "Caw! Begger-me! Yoo ban't ungry 'gaan be ee? Twadden long zince you ad breakfuss. I seed ee ayte vower aigs, dree gurt unks uv vat baacon, an a plaate uv vried tiddies. Un then yoo ayte dree payces uv braid marmalade an crayme."

Now t'other side started wi their vast baalers, two black fellas they wus. Caw wan uv um wus a laruppin gurt toad. Yer, I tellee when ee hove that there baal down yoo couldn zee en, no zooner didn letn go than yoo yerd'n knackin gin the bat. Ee sent down vower-vive baals 'n thicky batsman stapped two-dree, an jist titched wan so's ee went auver the slips fer vower rins.

This yer black fella didn like that traytement too well, so next baal ee draped'n bit short'n the ball vlied up'n 'it the batsman 'pon tap ees aid. Ee tooked auf ees 'elment an 'opped 'round rubbin ees aid. Yoo could zee eed-a-bin urted a bit. Ole 'Arry got proper stewer an 'ollered out too the batsman.

"Daun-ee let'n draw thick baal at ee like that, taake yer bat'n knack ee cross ees aid." Wist aut wus, when ee 'ollered out ee ad a mouth-vull uv daugh-caake, an ee showered the umman een vront uv us wi currants an caake-crumbs. Caw wudden er weeked. I thought sure erd it'n crost ees aid wi er umbreller. I looked t'other way, maade out ee wadn nort to do wi me.

When 'Arry ad vinished ees crib, an the umman een vront ad picked out most uv the zultanas'n currants out uv er 'air, ee zez, "Yer Jan, yoo zed yoo wus gwain too tell me all 'bout this yer gaame." "Aw auright", I zez, "Tis like this yer. These yer black fellas wot be bawlin now be tryin fer too 'it they dree sticks d'ye zee, an the batsman ev got too stap'n 'ittin, eef they kin, an rin 'zvaast they kin vore-n-back 'twain they sticks. Dye zee?" "Ees," ee zez, "but waas all theys other fellas stood round fer." "Aw theym the vielders", I told un. "They got too try too stap the baal when the batsman knacks'n, cus eef the baal rins too aydge uv the vield tiz vower rins, but eef they ketches the baal een their aans avore ee titches the groun' the batsman is gived out."

While I wus tellin'n all this wan uv the batsmen ad ees middle stump knacked out, an the bawler bawled a maiden auver. "Waas thaat yoo zay, Jan, that baggerin gurt toad ev knacked auver a lil maiden, caw darn my regs – ee ought too be 'shaamed uv ees zelf." So I ad bit more explainin too do. "Aw, ee got a long leg an a short leg ze zee", I zez. "Wot dye mayne Jan", ee zez, "Aw ken ee be anay gude wi waan layge longer 'n t'other?"

"Caw! waas think uv thaat", I zez, later on when their slaw-bawlers wus on. "Ee'v'a-got a zilly mid-auf een now." "Wadye mayne", zez 'Arry, "eef thicky bloke's zilly een ees aid ees no bizzness be'in there." "I zee ees gwain too put a man down een the gully now", I zez.

Poor ole 'Arry's zight idn too gude 's'naw zo ee zez "Caw this yer ole vield must be wiss'n our ol cow-park, 'ome too village where the local boyes plaay. I knaws there's a voo igh pits'n law-umps, an a voo cow-dabs where the cows lied the night avore, but us ebn got gurt gullies rinnin crostin."

"Caw, I zee they got a fella a'gwain too baal leg-breaks, I zee." 'Arry jumps up out uv ees zayte, nearly knacked the umman een vront wi ees zider jar. "I 'low tiz shaamaful", ee zez "Nere should be 'lowed, trying too break a vella's layge." Caw, I tell ee stright I ad a awful lot uv explainin too do. Talk 'bout a rinnin commentary. Yer! they there commentaters doan they yap. I 'low they could taalk the hinder leg auf a donkey.

Anyway arter nuther uv our fellas got out a black fella waalked out too bat fer Zumerzet. Their black fella rinned down an let vly the baal vaast as ee could, but ee could'n vrightn our fella. Ee knacked the baal all auver the plaace. Wan's, two's, drees, vowers 'n zebm gurt zixes, dree ub um right out uv the ground. When Zumerzet got too the end uv their overs, eed-a-scored wan underd'n' vive not out. Caw us all clapped 'n' chayerd'n all round the ground, an 'Arry 'ollered out "Come auver yer me buddy an av a zuck out uv me zider jar."

Anyhow een the eynde Zumerzet winned by Forty-zebm rins. Then us maade our way ome agaane.

✳ ✳ ✳

A Bit o' Binder String

MAY CROOK

Do ee mind Bill Bates as used to work ver Drake tu Badger's Aend?
Ther wernt a tool bout th farm thiccy veller couldn't maend
Vrim a 'ayvork to a 'arvester, or any mortal thing,
Ole Bill could awiz fix'n wi' a bit o' binder string.

❋ ❋

One day th' Friesian bull got out an' raged an' tore 'round
Nobody dared go near'n as 'e roared an 'ooked th' ground
Till Boss shouts "Bill! The bull's got out an' bin an brock 'ees ring."
So Bill lassoed th' begger wi' a bit o' binder string.

❋ ❋

Bill courted Mabel seven yer, an then 'e zaid, "Let's wed,
I'v got a table, an' zum cheers, an Granny's feather baid.
There's 'alf a ton o' tiddies upeen vaild as I c'n bring
An I'v made zum 'anzum door mats out o' thiccy binder string."

❋ ❋

"Well," Mabel zaid, "We'd best get wed vore they cut th'ay."
Zo they 'ad a slap-up wedding on the zem'teenth o' May.
But when they got to the church, Bill found 'eed gone an lost the ring.
Zo 'e 'ad t'marry Mabel wi' a loop o' binder string.

❋ ❋

Nex yer, a liddle maiden cum t'bless th'appy pair,
Wi' gurt blue eyes like saucers, an' a tuft o' ginger 'air.
An Bill zes tu Parson at the Baby's christenin,
"Zee, er 'air be jist the colour'v a bit o' binder string.

❋ ❋

Well time wen'on, an ole Bill died, an come to 'Eaven's door,
'E yerd em all a-zingin there an 'e were worrit zore.
An 'e zes t'gude St. Peter, "Zur I am'n nivver larned t'zing
I were awiz kep' zo busy mendin things wi' binder string.

❋ ❋

"Don't ee worry Bill," St. Peter zed, "the Gude Loard unnerstans
E'v bin a Carpenter, an likes tu zee volks use their 'ands.
An us be glad t'zee 'ee yer; we've plenty wat can zing,
But us needs a andy chap like thee – did'ee bring zum binder string?"

✳ ✳

Zo Bill do bide een 'Eaven now; he'm vury 'appy there
'Eve got a liddle workshop, roun be'ind St. Peter's cheer.
An while th' Angels play their 'arps, an all th' Saints do zing,
Bill mends th' liddle cherubs' toys – wi' bits o' binder string.

✳ ✳ ✳

Oh t' be a Blackburd

I zeed a liddle blackburd
A-zettin een a tree,
A purty liddle blackburd,
Za 'anzom az c'n be.

E wear'd a shiney black co-at,
A-glissenin een th' zun,
Jiy-vule zong vrum black drot,
Jiy-vule it wer zung.

Zing a zong t' laady-love,
A zong ov jiy an mirth,
All be well een 'eaven above
An all be well on earth.

Ef I cud be a blackburd,
A-zettin een a tree.
Wi all God's gifts aroun me
Oh, ow 'appy I wud be!

C.M.

Jan Cobbledick an' th' Rabbert

I be gwain t' tull ee bout ole Jan Cobbledick an th' rabbert. Yu zee ole Jan ad a maister likin ver rabbert – een a pie, stooed or baked – any way eez ole wumman cuked em, suited Jan.

Trouble wuz, Jan waddn wat yu'd call a hactive or a lousterin man – e didn like tu spuddlee over-much. Wat's more, e wuz noted ver kaipin eez money een eez pocket, zo e waddn over kain t'buy cartridges ver eez ole 12 bore gun, wat wuz all tied up roun th' stock wi binder cord.

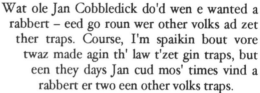

Wat ole Jan Cobbledick do'd wen e wanted a rabbert – eed go roun wer other volks ad zet ther traps. Course, I'm spaikin bout vore twaz made agin th' law t'zet gin traps, but een they days Jan cud mos' times vind a rabbert er two een other volks traps.

Now Artie Vanstone, th' gamekaiper on th' big estate, nawd all bout Jan's liddle tricks an e alzo nawd that Jan waddn above a bit o' pauchin now an then if e cuddn git no rabbert no other way.

One ov Artie's jobs, zides kaipin down th' varmints – wuz t'shet a vew rabbers, pigeons, pheasants an zich like ver th' larder up tu th' big 'ouse wer th' Squire, wat owned th' Estate, lived tu. Artie used tu 'ang em up overnight een th' ood shed back ov eez cottage. Course, e used to paunch an skin th' rabberts, cuz th' wimmin volk een th' big kitchen diddn like thic ole job.

Vunny thing waz, that vury oft wen Artie ad anged up zex or zeb'm rabberts, ther waz only vower or vive nex mornin. Arter this ad appened a vew times, Artie got t' thinkin – praps yu'v bin thinkin zame as e – that ole Jan Cobbledick might naw zummat bout they missing rabberts.

Jis bout this time, Artie's ole cat tooked zick an died – yu naws wats cummin nex, daun ee? Ace, Artie paunched an skinned th' ole cat an anged'n up een th' ood shed. Nex mornin, zure nuf, th' ole cat waz go.

That aiv'min Artie wen down th' pub, wer e waz purty zure eed vind ole Jan Cobbledick een eez uzual cornder. E diddn zay nort tu'n, but jis buyed isself a pint o' zider an ad a bit uv a tell wi Tommy Vinnecombe, th' landlord.

Arter a bit, Artie got spaikin bout ow eez ole cat ad tooked zick an died.

E alzo zaid, in a loud voice, that eed paunched an skinned th' ole cat wi th' idia uv veedin uv'n tu th' verrits. "But d'yu naw" zaid Artie, "wen I wen to get'n vrum th' ood ouse this mornin, wer I'd lef'n angin – e waz go."

Wi that, ther waz a zort uv chokin zound vrum th' cornder an up jumps Jan Cobbledick, lukin a bit green tu eez vace, an out e goes, az ef th' ole Dowel isself waz arter'n. An d'yu naw, nivver no more didn no rabberts disappear vrum Artie's ood shed – maakes ee think, daun et?

C.M.

The Cricket an' tha Bittle

HENRY BAIRD ('NATHAN HOGG')

A cricket ha zot a pin tap a tha aith,
An ha hollerd za lowd as ha cud squayl,
Wen a gurt black bittle a trapsin aun,
Ha tuk an scammil'd pin tap uv ez tayl.
Now kiss'n thee zee ware thee bee'st a gwayn,
Zed tha cricket, yu nasty vulty thing;
Yu zartinly can't be za mort'l deeve,
Bit wat! thit yu must hev a yerd ma zing.

✳ ✳

Tha bittle ha bust out intu a laff –
Wat! dee cal that zingin? aw, aw, zeth he!
If thee bees't a zinger, no kith uv mine,
Be tha black a ma cote shill zongsters be;
Tis nort bit a skritch, an wisser nur that, –
Ef I wis ta kick up zich awful rows
I'm zartin tha missus wid vurrit mer owt,
An nat allow mer ta bide in tha howse.

✳ ✳

Zes tha cricket yu hugly himprint twoad,
Iv'ry nite tha missus, avaur tha vi-er,
Zmile'th auver hur veace as hur yurs ma zing,
An lafths as I toon'th up hi-er an hi-er;
An as vur tha measter ha zmoak'th ez pipe,
An yu may zee be tha twink uv ez eye,
Thit vur vury glee as ha puf'th an blaw'th,
H'a widdn be happy zept I wur by.

✳ ✳

Tha bittle ha zed tha cricket wiz spared
Cuz ha jump'd away, an zed way skaurn,
Thit ez vur ez zul ha wiz lyk'd, a naw'd,
Vur a liv'd in tha howze iver zince ha wis baurn;
Bezaides vury auff wen ha vown et cole,
Ha'd ha'd stick'd eszul ta tha missus's hoze –
Hur'd car'd min up stairs, wen auff'n ha'd got
An zlayp'd way bothe awmin unde tha close.

✳ ✳

Then wan kintinid ta prayze up eszul,
Tha tuther kintinid ta du tha zeame;
An thare bothe measter an missus thay zot,
As if thay wiz draymin abowt tha vleame.
Ta last tha ole humman cort zight uv tha bothe,
An tha cricket ha squayl'd out hi-er an hi-er,
Wen hur shet out han tuk'd hole uv tha brush,
An zup'd tha bothe awmin inta tha vi-er.

✳ ✳

MORRIL

Wul, now warnin teake, bothe bittles and men,
An crickets an hummen tu,
If yu thinks za vury murch uv yerzul,
Tha wurdle thinks litt'l a yu;
An wile yu'm quardlin bowt wich ez tha best,
Stid uv stikkin ta wat yu'm meade,
Be tha vury wans yu may think yur vrends
Yu'll intu tha vi-er be drade.

✳ ✳ ✳

The Raft Race

JACK CONNABEER

Yer! Wot d'ye think I did laas Zinday? I went on me neighbours' raft wi a vew vriends, an went down the River Dart een this yer's raft race.

Yer! tis a brave ole journey too, I c'n tell ee. Bout teyn mile vrum Buckfastleigh too Totnes.

Me neighbour, George Thompson; ee told me siveral months agone, that ee wus gwain too enter a raft fer this yer caper. So I zez to en, "Yer! George I'll maake up wan uv yer crew." Well ventually there wus vive uv us; George, anuther neighbour Peter Lohmeyer, George's zin-in-law Peter an a vriend uv ee's Ian.

Wen missus yerred I wus gwain een fer this yer caper, er wus weeked's ell. "You gurt biddle-ayde, you mus be maaze. You want yer ayde zeein too."

Anyway, Zinday the zebmth uv Octawber arrived, twas middlin mild fer time uv yer, rained a bit early on:– well twuddn nort much reely, ony wot us caals a "dry drizzle". Anyway bye-n-bye the zin wus zhinin, an turned oot a bootiful day.

Wen us arrived out too Bucksleigh fer the start, there wus underds an thousans uv volks, everywhere, 'long the road, an een every vantage point 'long the river banks.

Us unloaded our raft een the medda 'long wi underds uv others. You niver zeed sich a collection uv rafts een all yer live. There wus oil-drums layshed toogether wi old ladders en bits uv 'ood. Plastix cans, ole lorry an tractor tubes blawed up an tied together een gurt long lines. Zum volks ad made up all zorts uv contraptions. Wan like a gurt lobster, 'nuther like a lil ole Austin Zebm. Then there wus wan like a airplane an anuther like a gurt army tank.

Zum volks dressed up een all zorts uv vancy costume. Lots uv wimmen an young maidens too. Zum uv they ony ad flimsy cloes on, an wen they got een the watter 'n got wet yuh could purd-nigh zee droo ot.

They zay there wus vower underd an vivty rafts eyntered this yer. Us wus number dree underd an ninty dree, zo us was 'mong the laast wans too go een the watter.

Caw! wen us started auf an luked down the river ee zeemed too be vull uv rafts an volks, wan pin tap t'other.

Zumbody zed too me "Wus there mach watter een the river Jan?"

"Well", I zed, "there wus quite a fair vlow uv river, but a lot more rocks 'n boulders."

Funny thing wus, evry time us ad too jump overboard 'cus there wuddn 'nough watter fer to vloat the raft, us allus zeemed too jump een watter up too our yers.

George, ee wus skipper like, ee zez too me. "Yer Jan, you knaws the river better than the rest o' us. You best be pilot an vind a way droo all the rocks an boulders." Zo yah zee, evry time us 'it a boulder, ee ollered too me "I thought you zed you knawed where all the rocks an boulders wus too!" "Ah ees", I ollered back, "the trouble is zum uv um bant where they wus too laas I went droo yer een a canoe."

Us gradully maade our way down river wi sivral minor mishaps like tryin too pule the raft over rocks an tredin on boulders an stones a slipper as zoap. Us valled down an knacked our knees an zhins an elbows.

Wance the raft nearly upsot an got vule uv watter so us ad too pule up on a gurt rock bee the zide uv the river 'n emp'm out.

Two-dree times us 'it a gurt boulder amidzhips an got turned right roun, zo us all turned too an paddled 'n long back-zie vorrards. Volk laafed too zee this yer caper, but then us would 'it another gurt stone an turn roun right way 'gain.

Us wus gwain long very well reely, us passed a lot uv rafts wot ad started long avore us. An wen I zeed zumbody I knawed, I ollered out to um. "Wot ev ee bin 'bout? You baint gwain very well bee ee."

Varder down river us zeed zum wot wus looking a bit coald 'n miserable arter bee-in in the watter a lot, specially eef they wuddn wearin the right zort uv cloes. Us ad all got on these yer "wet zuits". Yer I tell ee, tis a proper job, keep ee warm no matter ow many time yuh jumps een the river. Keeps all yer vital parts vrum gettin steeved wi the coald.

Us passed zum maidens on a raft that wus lukin a bit wuss fer wear. Us offered too give um a lift; but they zed "No thanks", prhaps they didn like the luke uv us.

Ventually us arrived at the vinish arter makin purdy gude time. I rekon everybody enjoyed therzelves – well most uv um anyway.

The best thing bout this yer caper is all the money wot it raises fer charity, too elp volks wot doant enjoy sich gude 'ealth as us. Though they may not be zo zaft een the ayde.

Vorriners zay "mad dowgs an Englishmen go out in the mid-day sun". Well zum us go an jump een a freezin coald river – jist fer vun!! I'd go 'gain nixt wik eef ther wus another race.

✳ ✳ ✳

Vrank an' th' Well

A vew yer agon, I used t'wet me oozle een a village pub wat av zince been tarted up an maade een tu wan o' they genuine ole country eens, wi 'oss brasses vrum Hong Kong an scampi an zich like. But een th' days I'm spaikin uv, yu cud get a gude drap o' zider an a butivul bit o' brade an chaise.

All th' watter wat they used cum vrum a well jist outzide th' back'ouse. Ther wuz a pump een th' kitchen an all th' waishin up wuz do'd wi this yer well watter wat wuz zo clain's a zmelt an zo zwait's a nit.

Now th' ole veller wat used tu 'elp roun th' plaace doin th' zwaipin an waishin th' mugs an gennerly maakin eezelv usevul wuz call'd Vrank. Course, eev bin gawn many a yer now, zo ee want mind me tullin ee bout th' well. Zims th' ole pump want zukin zuent; er want pullin up th' watter zo vitty az er ad do'd, zo Vrank, ee lifted up th' cover over th' well t'av a luke down, t'zee eef ther wuz ort blockin t'aind uv th' pipe wat th' watter wuz zuked up droo. Course, et wuz all dark down een th' well an Vrank cuddn zee nort, zo ee got down on eez belly an 'anged eez aid down een th' well tu av a better luke-zee. Jist az ee wuz doin o't, ee wuz took'd wi a vit o' coughin. I 'spect twuz th' douse wat zet'n auv.

Now I should tull ee that Vrank ad valse taith wat didn vit too vitty – ace yu'm right! Yu naws wat 'appened nex, dawn ee? Out cum eez taith an plop right down een th' watter at th' bottom uv th' well. Now Vrank didn like tu tull volks wat an ole vule eed bin, lettin eez taith drap een th' well, zo wen volks axed'n wer eez taith wuz tu, ee jist zaid eed losted uv um an none o' th' reglers tu th' pub nawed that th' watter wat waished ther mugs ad vust waished ole Vrank's taith.

Arter a couple o' yer, th' volks een th' Council up t' Exter, zided that th' village ud be better auv wi watter wat cumm'd out uv a ole pipe, all th' way vrum zum rezzevoy miles away an that th' village volk wuz gwain t'av t'pay ver't, whereaz avore times, they'd got it vree out o' ther wells wat nivver dried up, drout or no drout.

Course, th' pub ad thiz yer mains watter az they calls it, an Vrank didn av t'do no more pumpin, but th' reglers zaid that they didn like thiz yer ole mains watter zum'ow, they zaid ther waddn th' vlavour een it an even th' mugs wat ole Vrank waished, addn got quite th' zame sparkle az they ad wen they wuz waished een th' well watter.

Wish ee well ver now then me luvvers, I got t' be gwain aum now, but I'll zee ee agin.

C.M.

Rules and Regillations of the new MILK and DAIRIES ORDER according to 'Jan Stewer'
A. J. Coles 1876 – 1965

RULES and REGILLATIONS

for the hine-drance and bewilderment of all Varmers and sitch as keeps cows; and to provide 'em with zummat to occupy their spare time and use up their spare cash if they've got any.

The following Rules and Regillations is to be fulfilled in regards to all Shippins, Sheds, or any plaaces where cows is kept for the purpose o' being milked; and also in regards to all they what do's the milking and all their friends and relations.

INSPECTORS

All cowsheds must be ready for inspection at any time o' day or night by eether o' the following people:–

The Local Sanitary Authority, Inspector of Cruelty to Animals, Skule Attendance Ossifer, Council Surveyor, Medical Ossifer of Health, Boy Scouts, Girl Guides, the Village Policeman, Town Crier, Rate Collecter, Cap'm o' the Vire Brigade, the Mimber o' Parlyment, the Distric' Nurse and the President o' the Church Council. If eether-one o' these people pays a visit to the varm the varmer must leave whatever he's about and go around and assist 'em to poke their noses into his business. If he don't he'll be vined vive pound.

All cowsheds must face towards the zouth. Any what faces towards the north mus' be turned around or pulled down and putt up fresh. Ten pound vine fer all cowsheds what faces in the wrong derection.

Every cowshed must have a winder oppozyte each crub, so's the cows can look out and view the scenery, and the winders mus' be clained twice a wik. Vorty shullins vine fer durty winders.

All winders mus' have blines to pull up and down in case the zun shude be too hot.

All cowsheds mus' be furnished in a proper manner with aisy cheers and a sofa, so's the cows can rest comferable arter meals. A pianner or orgin shude be pervided if the varmer or eether of his chaps can play 'en. If not, there shude be a grannyfone or the wireless, as cows is very partial to music.

Ev'ry cow mus' be pervided with a looking-glass, to zee if her horns is on straight. Powder puffs is not compulsory but is highly recommended.

All cowsheds mus' be pervided with bath-rumes with hot an' cold watter; wan bath-rume to every three cows. Vive pound vine fer every bath-rume not pervided.

The vloors of all cowsheds mus' be covered with carpet. Linoleum won't do, cus it strikes cold to the cows' veet, and is hard to lie upon. A doormat mus' be putt to every door for the chaps to wipe their boots upon bevore they goes in.

Picshers shude be hanged around the walls to make the plaace bright and cheerful, but not photos o' the varmer or his misses, cus cows has feelings.

A bell mus' be pervided fer each cow so's he can ring fer the varmer if he shude want aught in the night.

TREATMENT OF COWS

Everything must be done to make the cow's life 'appy and comferable. Varmers will be vined vive pound if their cows is looking miserable and fed up.

Every cow must be gived a bath fust thing in the morning. The watter mus' be eighty-nine degrees hot and ninety degrees cold.

When took out o' the bath the cows must be dried very careful and disted all auver with vi'let powder. Care mus' be took that the watter is well aired bevore the cows is put into the bath.

Cows mus' be 'lowed to zit down when they'm being milked; or if they prefers to walk about the milker mus' move according. Cows muzzen be vexed upon no account. Anybody vexing the cows will be vined vive pound.

Every cow mus' be supplied with a pocket-ankcher, with his name in the corner so's they shan't get mixed up. Cows mus' never be 'lowed to blaw their nawses on wantother's hankchers. That's the way colds is spread.

Every cow must have a toothbrish of his awn, and his teeth mus' be clained twice a day.

Cows muzzen be made to sleep in the dark if they daun' like it. Lectrisical light shude be fixed up if possible; otherwise lamps shude be hanged about the plaace.

Cows mus' not be made to drink out o' the same buckets as the chaps. If there id'n enough buckets to go aound the cows mus' have fust drink. If the cows don't zeem to fancy drinking out o' buckets they shude have tay-cups.

Cows mus' not be turned out into a vield bevore the grass has been properly disted, becus the dist gets into the milk and then the varmer will be vined vive pound. Brooming off the grass will be sufficient if the vield is more than hunderd yards from the road. All flies mus' be drove away bevore the cows is turned out becus flies brings germs.

Cows mus' be pervided with slippers if the grass is damp. Otherwise they ketches cold.

If a cow ketches cold he mus' be made to wear flannel next his skin and have a hot-water bottle nights. If he coughs twice the varmer mus' give notice to the Chairman o' the Skule-Board and send a report to the Inspecter of Weights and Measures.

REGILLATIONS FOR VARMERS

All varmers mus' zee that their cows' eyes is properly attended to, and if they'm short-zighted they mus' be pervided with sparticles. Otherwise they'm ap' to overlook the mangel and go short, and the varmer will be vined vive pound.

If any mimber o' the varmer's vamily shude get bunions, housemaid's knee or a floating kidney the cows mus' not be milked until permission have been got from the Bishop or a Churchwarden.

No varmer shall be 'lowed to shift his cows from wan vield to the next without he've got a gun-licence and vifty cigarette cards. If he do he'll be vined vive pound.

REGILLATIONS FOR MILKERS

No one shall be allowed to milk a cow unless he've got a vourth standard sustificate and can say the twice-times table back'erds.

Every chap employed milking mus' wear coller and tie, and he muzzen go milking mornings wai'out shaving. If he'm in the habit o' wearing wiskers he mus' zee that the ends don't dangle in the milk, cus that causes contamination.

Milkers mus' take care to wipe their boots when they goes into the cowsheds, and again when they comes out.

Milkers mus' remember 'tis bad behaviour to sit down bezide a cow without axing he to sit down fust. After all, a cow's a vemale, never mind how many legs he've got, and shude be traited as sitch.

Chaps mus' be careful to avoid braithing while they'm milking as their breath might help to turn the milk zour.

Milkers is not to spaik cross to the cows. If they wants a cow to move wan zide or tother they mus' say "plaise;" not, "Git over, you ramshackle zon of a cross-breed oss-radish." Cows is muty-'arted, and it spoils their milk to be spoke to that way.

If the cow flinks his tail in the milker's eye or putts his voot in the bucket the milker is 'lowed to say, "Bother it," or, "Dear, dear." If he says, "Darn your stoobid eyes I'll skin you alive if you daun' bide still" he'll be vined vive pound. And if 'tis zummin wiss than that he'll be vined more, up to tain pound, according to the wiss-ness.

NOTICE

The above regillations is just to go on with. If it should be found that any varmers and cowkeepers is still making a living the ole Parlyment will think out some more.

❋ ❋ ❋

"Rules and Regillations" was written in 1927 when "Jan" was a farmer at Poole Farm, Whitestone near Exeter.

Biographical Notes

Henry Baird

Author of *Letters and Poems tu es Brither Jan by 'Nathan Hogg'*

Henry Baird rarely mentioned rural matters in his many dialect poems, but confined himself to events in Exeter, where he was a bookseller in St. Martin's Lane.

He wrote about the bread riots in 1847, visits of important personages, the washerwomen, soldiers and servant girls and many other matters. Because of his concentration on Exeter, he has left us, in his own form of phonetic spelling, a valuable record of the pronunciation of the dialect of the city in the mid 19th century.

We are told that he was of swarthy complexion and had a cast in one eye. He dedicated his first 'Nathan Hogg' to His Royal Highness Prince Louis Lucien Bonaparte, who wrote to him saying –

"My Dear Mr. Baird,

About your dedicating your book to me, I shall be very happy to accept it; and as far as concerns my humble individual opinion about your ability in the Devonshire Dialect, I can only say that all the most intricate and difficult questions about the pronunciation and other grammatical proprieties of this very interesting dialect have been answered by you in such a manner as to enable me to adopt several of the modifications of the orthography, the which certainly I could never have attained except through a person thoroughly acquainted, as you, in my opinion, undoubtedly are, with the peculiarities of this curious form of the English speech.

Believe me, yours very sincerely,

L. L. Bonaparte."

According to a *Biographical Sketch* in a 1902 reprint of the first edition of 'Nathan Hogg', Henry Baird moved to London in the "hope of obtaining more profitable employment", but "he did not survive the change and on 3rd May, 1881, died of consumption aged about 52 years."

Henry Baird left us not only a priceless record of Devon dialect, but also a most graphic social account of his time.

A. J. Coles – "Jan Stewer"

Author of many dialect books too numerous to mention here.

Two of his best known books, *A Parcel of ol' Crams* and *In Chimley Corner* have recently been republished by Alan Sutton Publishing Ltd. The contents of these books and others by "Jan" have been read by several generations of Devonians.

Although not a Devonian, having been born in Woolwich, London, his love of Devon dialect, originally stimulated as a child on holidays in our county, developed into an understanding and knowledge of great authority.

A. J. Coles was one of those remarkable people of whom it is said that they are a 'Jack of All Trades' except, in his case, he was a 'Master of All'. He was, at various times, newspaper correspondent and editor, schoolmaster, farmer, entertainer, author, actor, poet, songwriter, ventriloquist, playwright and hotelier.

"Jan's" great contribution to the Devon dialect is that through his writings he kept alive and stimulated interest in this part of our Devon heritage. He never patronised and it is a tribute to him that, among the most ardent readers and reciters of his many stories, the majority of them were and still are the people about whom he wrote.

May Crook

Unfortunately not much is known about her at present, other than that she lived at Dalwood in East Devon and was a member of the Womens' Institute.

Her two contributions to this book came to Clem Marten through correspondence with the Lakeland Dialect Society, where advice was being sought by the Devon Dialect Society about its Constitution.

May Crook was such a gifted writer of Devon dialect that it is to be hoped that more of her work will be discovered.

W. Gregory Harris

Author of *West-Country Volk*, etc.

Gregory Harris, born in Tavistock, was a Wesleyan minister in Torquay, Devon and Bridgwater, Somerset.

His poem *Our Dem'shur Spaich* is noteworthy inasmuch that it includes many Devon dialect words and phrases. However, in one or two instances the Somerset dialect finds its way into the poem. For instance, most Devonians are unlikely to use the word 'du' (do) in the way Gregory Harris has, but that is not to say that the dialect of Somerset does not mingle with that of Devon near the county borders.

William Weeks

Author of *Bits o' Broad Devon, Devonshire Yarns* and the song, *A Mortal Unlucky Old Chap.*

Although perhaps not as well known as some Devon dialect writers, William Weeks ranks amongst the best of them. He was born in the village of Dolton near Hatherleigh in Devon and learned to speak the dialect as his 'first' language. Later he became senior lecturer in English and Mathematics at St. Luke's Teachers' Training College in Exeter – now a part of the University.

Publisher's Note: The above biographical notes are as they appeared in the original edition of this book.

Jack Connabeer

A true Devonian, and proud of his ancestry, Jack Connabeer was born into a farming family at Millcombe in 1923 and lived in the same parish (Berry Pomeroy) for 35 years. He then moved to nearby Dartington to take over Hood Barton and continued farming there, helped by his wife and four sons, until eventually retiring in the year 2000 and moving to South Brent.

Apart from his great love of farming, Jack has always been very interested in the Devonshire dialect and has not only given talks on the subject, but has also written a number of articles and short stories for the *Moreton News,* the now-defunct Devon Dialect Society and various Young Farmers' publications to name but a few – using, of course, his own Devonshire dialect! For a while he was also involved in amateur dramatics and once had the great pleasure of meeting the son of Jan Stewer – Mr H. A. T. Coles.

Jack is also proud of his 30-year involvement with The Devon Rural Skills Trust, which was set up to revive traditional practices and to teach others of the rural skills of Devon before they died out and in order to maintain them for posterity. Indeed, Jack is currently its chairman and takes great delight in seeing some of the Trust's former students having themselves become teachers of the rural skills, some with their own practices. As Jack says, this proves that the Trust's original aims have been successfully achieved.

Mike Lang

Clement Marten 1916 – 1986

Author of *The Devonshire Dialect*, written in 1972.

His parents and relatives spoke Devon dialect and one aunt in particular, Aunty Bea, who gave public readings of dialect, generated a lifetime interest in the subject.

As a child, Clem lived in Plymouth and Exeter, and spent all his holidays on the farms of relatives in North Devon and North Cornwall, whose boundaries are near the upper reaches of the River Tamar. Out of self-protection, he adopted the speech of the people of the area; otherwise he could have been thought to be a bit superior and, as Gregory Harris says in his poem, might be taken to be one of "they there dapper chaps, zo mincin in their spaich", so Devon dialect became his second language.

He was working in London when World War Two was declared and became an ARP Warden. Later he joined the R.A.F. as a photographer in the recognisance division, going on to serve in North Africa and Italy. It was at this time that his mother died in an air raid over Plymouth. After the war, he trained as a commercial artist, specialising in photographic retouching which he'd learnt in the R.A.F. He later published a book titled *The Airbrush Manual.*

Over the next 30 years he had a number of jobs, including driving instructor, manager of a holiday caravan site and a fabric shop, steward of a golf club, a sales rep for language laboratories, a draughtsman for a country estate and working in a factory making precision equipment. During this period he also set up his own photographic business, ran a guest house, old peoples' home and took in students (all in the same house, but at different times) and, latterly, started his own advertising agency in Exeter, which he continued to run up until his retirement.

His interest in the Devonshire dialect grew and he eventually initiated the formation of The Devon Dialect Society, of which he was its Chairman. He broadcasted on BBC radio about Devon dialect from 1973 to 1986. He also became very interested in the etymology of Devon dialect and built up an extensive collection of words and phrases, many of them contributed by listeners of his broadcasts for which he was grateful.

Sue Quick

Glossary

Words marked * are examples of metathesis, the reversal of vowels and consonants, common in Devon dialect. Other examples are: urn – run; urd – red; Urgiment – Regiment; burd – bread; crips – crisp; burge – bridge; Urchet – Richard.

ace, iss, ees yes
aend end
agon ago
aisy cheers easy chair
aith hearth
aive heave
ankcher handkerchief
anyels angels
anzum handsome
appledrane wasp
***apse** hasp, fastening on door or gate
avenin evening
***axe** ask

backalong previously, the road behind
back'ouse scullery, back kitchen (The front door of a Devon farmhouse was rarely used, except for funerals, weddings and 'upzettins' i.e. Christenings. Everyone entered and left the farmhouse by the door in the 'back'ouse'.)
backsivore back to front – see vore
bellises bellows
baint be it not, is not, will not
be am
biddle heavy wooden mallet

bide stay, from Anglo Saxon word 'bidan' – to stay
bile boil
binder horsedrawn harvesting machine
binder cord cord for binding sheaves
bissle beastly, i.e. dirty
bittle beetle
blare shout, scold
bliddy waryers bloody warriors, i.e. wallflowers
blooth bloom
boy's love a shrub
braave brave, fine, well, commendable
bullicks bullocks

car'd carried
cauch slop, sticky (also messy or sticky, from 'caucheries' – medicinal slops fed to invalids.)
chucked choked
clapper claw a scold
clink gaol, prison
clunk drink
***crilly greens** curly greens, curly kale
crost across
crub crib, feed trough

dapper correct, on best behaviour
datchin' thatching
deeve deaf
dimpsey twilight, evening (also called 'candle-teenin', the time of tending to the candles.)
ditchin' ditching, i.e. cleaning out ditches
do's, doos does, carries out
douse dust
Dowel the Devil
drade thrown, drawn
dreckly soon
dree three
drench pour medicine down an animal's throat
drexil threshold
droo through
drot throat
dungcart wheeled cart for carrying animal manure (dung) to field for spreading

eezel his self, himself
ee him or thee

flibberts small pieces e.g. the song 'Tavistock Goosey Fair'
flink a quick movement like a whip lash
flittermouse bat

gabbin' talking
go gone
graizey greasy
grub food
*****gurt** great
gwain going

harbs herbs
he, her are interchangeable in

Devon dialect
heckamal, hackamul tomtit
his, hers as he, her
hollerd shouted, called
humman woman

jis just

kidney bains kidney beans, string or French beans
kintindid contended
kiss'n can'st not
kitch catch
kith relatives
kittle kettle

larn learn
lewth lew, the side sheltered from wind and rain
licky-brath leek broth or stew
lousterin' hard work, being busy

maester master
maiden teenage girl (baby girl – cheel (child).)
mangel mangleworzel root vegetable used for cattle feed
maunderin' muttering
mazed mad, foolish
mite little
mitchin absence from school
mortal very much
mouthspaich dialect
mumblin talking quietly to oneself
muty arted softhearted, easily upset

nawd past tense of know
niddick hollow in back of neck
nit nut
nort nothing

ood wood
olt hold
oozle whistle, throat (throat or mouth, "wet yer oozle" – have a drink.)
orchits orchards
*ossifer officer

passon parson
pauchin poaching
paunch remove intestines etc
pays peas
pinny raidins penny readings (Country folk, often illiterate, would pay a penny to attend a meeting where they could hear stories read aloud.)
primrosen plural of primrose
pun (pin) tap upon the top
purt, purty pretty, meaning 'almost'

quot squat, sit down

rabbert rabbit
regillations regulations
rezzevoy reservoir
rind ran
ringworms skin disease caused by fungus

scad shower of rain
scammil scramble
scat break, throw
sclum scratch
sherds small pieces of broken pottery
shet shoot
sight a lot, much more
sitch such
skriddicks small pieces almost worthless

skritch screech
'sno dost thou know
sparticles spectacles
spuddlee to busy oneself
spurred reared up
squayle squeal
stag a cock, especially in N. Devon
stooed stewed
suent see 'zuent'

tell chat
tetties/tiddies potatoes
thick abbreviation of 'thicky' meaning 'that'
thust thirst
titchin touching
toads commonly used in a derogatory sense
towse busy
traade trade (almost worthless, as 'trade goods' which were shipped abroad to exchange for spices, ivory, skins, etc.)
traipsin walking slowly, aimlessly (a 'traipse' was a 'woman of the streets'.)
tu to, sometimes 'at'
twink twinkle

urge retch, vomit

varmints vermin
verrits/vurrits ferrets
vew (voo) few
vexed upset
vittles victuals, food
vitty, viddy correct
voot foot
vore front, along, towards, furrow (From the Celtic word 'vor' meaning a furrow or way through. Hence many Fore Streets in Devon and Cornwall.)

vourty forty
vulty filthy

waysgoose outing, day out, picnic, short holiday
weskit waistcoat
whate wheat
whoam home
wisht/whisht bewitched, strange, pale, in poor health
wiss worse
wisser 'more worse'
*wops wasp
worrit worried
wurdle world

yer year, ear, here, hear

zackly exactly ('Not zackly' – feeling unwell – possibly through looking through the bottoms of too many glasses.)
zartin certain
zeed saw, past tense of to see
zided decided
zim seem, i.e. think, believe
zittee sit thee
zmelt smelt, a species of fish
zuent, suent operating smoothly, without difficulty
zukin sucking
zummat something
zup sweep

A dictionary of over 800 Devon dialect words and phrases is included in *The Devonshire Dialect* by the same author. This book is still in print and is obtainable from all good booksellers or direct from the publishers (Price: £3.99).

Acknowledgements

Grateful thanks are expressed to all those people who gave permission to reprint specific stories/poems that add so much to this book.
Special thanks are due to Mr H. A. T. Coles for permission to reproduce the three stories included in this book that were written by his late father – A. J. Coles ('Jan Stewer').
Frank Reynolds' cartoons reproduced by permission of Punch Limited.

(In the first edition of this book the author also expressed thanks to Mr G. Paley – formerly Librarian of the Westcountry Studies Library and at the Devon & Exeter Institution – who has since died. The author added that his extensive knowledge had been of great help to him in researching Devon dialect and for biographical information.)